ALIEN CULTURES

MANDARIN

THREE'S A CROWN

Society on the various worlds of the CETIAN IMPERIUM is based entirely upon the TRIUNE. The concept of the TRIUNE permeates Cetian life, from its sovereign body, a ruling triumvirate of Princes known as the TRIPLE CROWN COURT, to a convention which underpins Cetian society in general, THE TRIUNE MARRIAGE.

While the TRIUNE MARRIAGE has certainly become a context for the framework of law in the matter of property inheritance, its true origins lie in a simple fact of Cetian biology: it takes three Cetians to make a nymph.

This wasn't always the case. In the distant past, nymphs were born normally, from a single, self-impregnating parent, a time referred to in Cetian archaeobiology as 'The Era of the Single Parent Family.'

For Interpreter Zchhcz of the Tau Ceti Imperium, the system had been working well. He had made a celebrated Engagement Pact with Analyst Exxus and Architect Vret. Pledge Crystals had been exchanged, and their courtship, by Earth standards, was in its fiftieth year.

With the date of the Triune Marriage set, Analyst Exxus had only to finish his monumental translation of THE CANTICLES OF LLIGINNER, Architect Vret to complete work on the second PEDESTAL FORUM, while Interpreter Zchhcz had only to return from the FOMALHAUT ORE DISCUSSIONS.

If a day comes when human society is allowed full interchange with that of the Cetian Imperium, we will learn more on that day than during the millennium.

We will learn that genetic material floats between the stars, and wherever an eddy or a pocket may form, or an environment offers an exploitable nutrient, some kind of lifeform will begin to establish itself. We will discover that a genetic programme which we share with butterflies, although dormant in us, gives the people of Capella IV the colours of butterfly wings. We will realise that this panspermia was the first true space travel, and when we finally meet alien life we may find some familiar genes waving back at us. The creatures may not seem so alien after all.

But, knowing our record, we probably won't look for beauty. We will see those waving genes as threatening fists. Like Jan Van Owen, some of us will inevitably be seeking to give the aliens enemy status.

Had the laboratory studies ordered by Van Owen upon the captive Skizz been motivated by interest in an alien species for its own sake, it would still have been an outrage, but they might have found the Clam Gene. More accurately, the gene which causes clams and Cetians alike to begin life as males and end up as females.

And while studying more deeply the strange complexity of the alien blood they might have found something more astonishing than any familiar gene. An almost perfect, benevolent parasite.

THE BIOREGULATOR

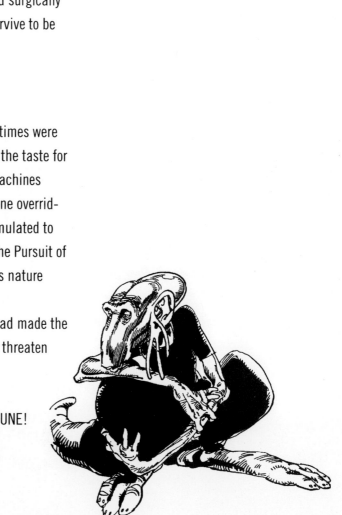

The BIOREGULATOR does not kill or emaciate its host, or promote illness that would alert medical science to expunge it. Instead, it gives support to every aspect of health in the host, whilst extending life expectancy tenfold. Thus, it ensures long and comfortable life for itself.

Nobody knows where the BIOREGULATOR came from, or when. All that is known is that under its protection, life is better. Life is longer, life is – like the parasite itself – almost perfect.

Almost, but not quite. There turns out to be a special problem with extreme longevity in Cetians. Gestation time is also extended, and before term can be reached, the embryo is destroyed by the mother's immune system. For a time it seemed as though the gift of life bestowed upon Ceti by the BIOREGULATOR was at the same time a death sentence for the species. With no new nymphs born, extinction would be guaranteed!

At the eleventh hour, it was discovered that nymphs removed surgically at one-third term and transferred to two subsequent hosts would survive to be born. With three parents instead of just one, the species was safe.

Thus, began the TRIUNE.

By and large, society under the TRIUNE burgeoned, but extended lifetimes were giving the Cetians more time for leisure, and as leisure grew, so did the taste for it. The tedious business of government was slowly handed over to machines under the supreme control of THE MATRIX, a computer system with one overriding remit: to uphold the CETIZEN'S CHARTER. The CHARTER was formulated to defend, firstly, the inviolable rights of Cetizens to Life, Liberty, and the Pursuit of Happiness. And secondly, to protect any system or process that by its nature was supportive of the aforementioned CHARTER.

First among these supportive systems, the institution that had made the very continuity of the species possible, was of course the TRIUNE. To threaten the TRIUNE was to imperil at once every provision of the CHARTER.

Nothing, but NOTHING must be allowed to jeopardise the TRIUNE!
Not even LOFAT YOGHURT...

Jim Baikie

prelude

SKIZZ, also known as Interpreter Zchhez of the Tau Ceti Imperium, had been en route to the Fomalhaut Ore Discussions when his ship's lymph-batteries perforated, leaving him with only one option; to take the Tramp-Route to Fomalhaut. Luckily he had given himself the usual huge margin for error, so there was still a chance he'd make it to his destination in time.

But the Tramp-Route is the most tedious, unspectacular flightpath imaginable, and the bored Tau-Cetian was tempted to take an illegal short-cut through the Restricted Belt.

At the time, be blamed his crash on the failure of his makeshift repairs, but whatever the reason, control was lost, and his ship came flaming out of Light-Space on a collision course with the worst Hellworld in the Restricted Belt.

To avoid the unthinkable prospect of Cetian technology falling into the hands of savages, Skizz knew that regulations would now require the total destruction of his grounded craft. Desperately he beseeched the ship's computer to open the hatch first, and let him out.

In an impossible lapse of procedure, the computer agreed, and Skizz was left alone upon a hostile world, marooned on the mean streets of Burmygam.

It was indeed a hell-world! The air was too thick, he couldn't digest the food, and the indigenous inhabitants seemed little more than brutes. Had he not encountered a certain good human, Roxy O'Rourke, who introduced him to Lofat Yogurt, he would certainly not have lived to meet a certain bad human, Mr. Jan Van Owen.

In the days that followed he would wish many times that he had not lived to meet Jan Van Owen.

Van Owen had a deep hatred of anyone who wasn't a white Anglo-Saxon, and Skizz was, well, a beige Tau-Cetian. It all came to a head one night on Spaghetti Junction. Three things were flying that night, bullets, a giant Cetian rescue ship, and ... with the aid of Cornelius, Van Owen himself. Then Roxy, Cornelius and Loz said goodbye, and the miracle went away.

Skizz was returning home, his troubles over at last ... ... or were they?

Nine years on, he's not so sure.

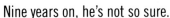

"I CONFESS I ATE SMALL QUANTITIES OF BABY-FOOD."

"WITH WHAT RESULT?"

"REGURGITATION. MY STOMACH WAS INCOMPATIBLE."

"HOW, THEN, DID YOU SURVIVE UPON THE HELL-WORLD?"

"ROXY FOUND AN ACCEPTABLE FOOD. SHE CALLED IT **LO-FAT YOGURT.** AFTER THAT, I BEGAN TO TOLERATE BABY FOOD."

"THIS... **LOFATYOGURT...** CONTAINED A LIVE CULTURE OF MICRO-ORGANISMS?"

"I BELIEVE SO, BUT..."

"YOU UNDERSTAND WHY YOU ARE UNDER SCRUTINY?"

"I AM TOLD THAT THE MICRO-ORGANISM REPLICATES STILL IN MY GUT. THE **BIO-REGULATOR** CANNOT ERADICATE IT. BUT—"

"THE **BIO-REGULATOR** HAS PROTECTED US FOR CENTURIES. YOU MUST APPRECIATE OUR CONCERN OVER AN **IMPERVIOUS ORGANISM.** THE COUNCIL FEARS—"

"PLEASE, COUNCILLOR! I FEEL **EXTREMELY WELL!**"

"--THAT IF UNCHECKED, THIS... LOFATYOGURT MAY QUICKLY BECOME AN **EPIDEMIC.**"

THE PLANET IS CALLED **GARP.**

NOW IN A WINTERING ORBIT, ITS SURFACE CRACKLES WITH UNIMAGINABLE COLD. IN THE THIN CANOPY, METHANE CRYSTALS SPARK AS DIM STAR-BLOWN LIGHT FROM THE SECOND OF THE TRIPLE SUNS MOCKS THE REMEMBERED WARMTH OF **TAU CETI PRIME.**

NOBODY BORN UNDER **TAU CETI PRIME** WOULD **EVER** COME HERE.

WELL, **ALMOST** NOBODY...

IS NAME IS **BAZZER NORMAN**. HE IS A LONG WAY FROM QUEENSLAND, AUSTRALIA.

HIS STOMACH IS SHRINKING, AND HIS HEAD IS SPLITTING.

HE HAS HAD IT UP TO **HERE** WITH THE 'OLD COUNTRY'.

HELLO?

WHO'S THERE?

CRIPES, MATE. YOU HAD ME THINKING THEM COPPERS WERE BACK!

ER...YOU WANT TO WARM UP BY THE FIRE...?

NO TUCKER, I'M AFRAID.

STONE ME! **THAT** LOOKS ALL RIGHT!

BACK HOME THEY BLAME YOU POMS FOR ALL THE RABBITS IN AUSTRALIA.

ME, I'M JUST GLAD THIS ONE GOT LEFT HERE.

I AIN'T **COMPLAININ'** OR NOTHIN', SPORT...

BUT YOU AIN'T EXACTLY...

YOU AIN'T MUCH OF AN AFTER-DINNER SPEAKER, ARE YOU.

LOTS OF TIMES I'VE WISHED I WAS IN AUSTRALIA.

WHAT DO YOU MEAN, I CANNOT HAVE THE ICE-FRAGMENT **INSIDE** THE HABITATION MODULE?

ALAS, THERE ARE **DANGERS**. WE WILL PLACE IT, FOR YOUR PLEASURE, AS NEAR AS MAY BE.

IT LOOKS **STUPID** OUT THERE!

WHAT POSSIBLE DANGER COULD THERE BE:...?

WE HAVE DETECTED CYANOGEN POCKETS CLOSE TO THE SURFACE...

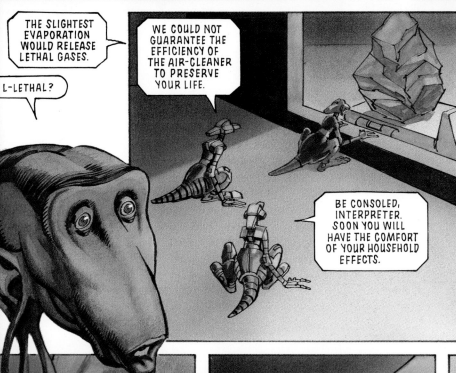

THE SLIGHTEST EVAPORATION WOULD RELEASE LETHAL GASES.

L-LETHAL?

WE COULD NOT GUARANTEE THE EFFICIENCY OF THE AIR-CLEANER TO PRESERVE YOUR LIFE.

BE CONSOLED, INTERPRETER. SOON YOU WILL HAVE THE COMFORT OF YOUR HOUSEHOLD EFFECTS.

IN THE GLARE OF THE CARRIER'S DESCENT-BURN, THE ICE-FRAGMENT SPARKLES, AND ONCE MORE...

I SEE IT! I SEE IT **AGAIN**!

THE **FACE**!

"SAY **GIRL**."

RAHK-SEE!

R-ROXY?

INTERPRETER, MAY WE ADVISE?

YOU ARE DWELLING OVERLONG UPON THE EVENTS OF THE **HELLWORLD**.

FOR ONCE, INTERPRETER SKIZZ IS IN AGREEMENT...

THERE IS A **HELLWORLD**.

AND INTERPRETER SKIZZ IS UNABLE TO STOP DWELLING UPON IT.

CORNELIUS, WHERE DID... SKIZZ... **COME FROM,** IN HIS SPACE SHIP?

WALES.

HE WAS MY BEST PAL EVER, SKIZZ WAS.

WALES?

THAT'S, ER...THAT'S NOT, Y'KNOW...

EXACTLY IN OUTER SPACE.

THIS WALES IS.

SKY'S WRONG TONIGHT, BUT IT'S A LONG WAY OFF.

FURTHER THAN **BOURNEMOUTH,** EVEN.

HANG ABOUT! DO YOU MEAN **WHALES?** THE CONSTELLATION OF **CETUS, THE WHALE?**

SETTEE, THAT'S IT. **TOE SETTEE.** YOU KNOW ABOUT STARS? I DIDN'T, TILL SKIZZ SHOWED ME WHERE IT WAS.

TOE...**TAU! TAU** CETI?

IF THE UNIVERSE IS INDEED INFINITE, ALL THINGS MUST BE POSSIBLE.

BAZZER REFLECTS THAT IT MUST THEREFORE BE POSSIBLE FOR CORNELIUS CARDEW TO INVENT A STORY ABOUT ALIEN VISITATION.

BUT THAT WOULD NOT EXPLAIN WHY BAZZER FEELS ICY FINGERS WALKING UP HIS SPINE.

CORNELIUS...

CAN I HAVE A CLOSER LOOK AT YOUR KEEPSAKE?

YOU SHARED YOUR CAMP WITH ME.

YOU CAN HAVE IT FOR FIVE MINUTES.

DUNNO WHAT THE BUTTONS DO. SKIZZ WOULD KNOW.

WHAT... WHAT WERE SKIZZ'S HANDS LIKE?

JUST...I'D SAY, JUST LIKE **HANDS.** EXCEPT... THERE WAS LESS FINGERS.

YEH, AND MORE THUMBS.

LOOKS LAID OUT FOR FOUR DIGITS EACH SIDE.

IF I USE BOTH HANDS, I CAN JUST ABOUT REACH HALF OF 'EM...

STONE ME!

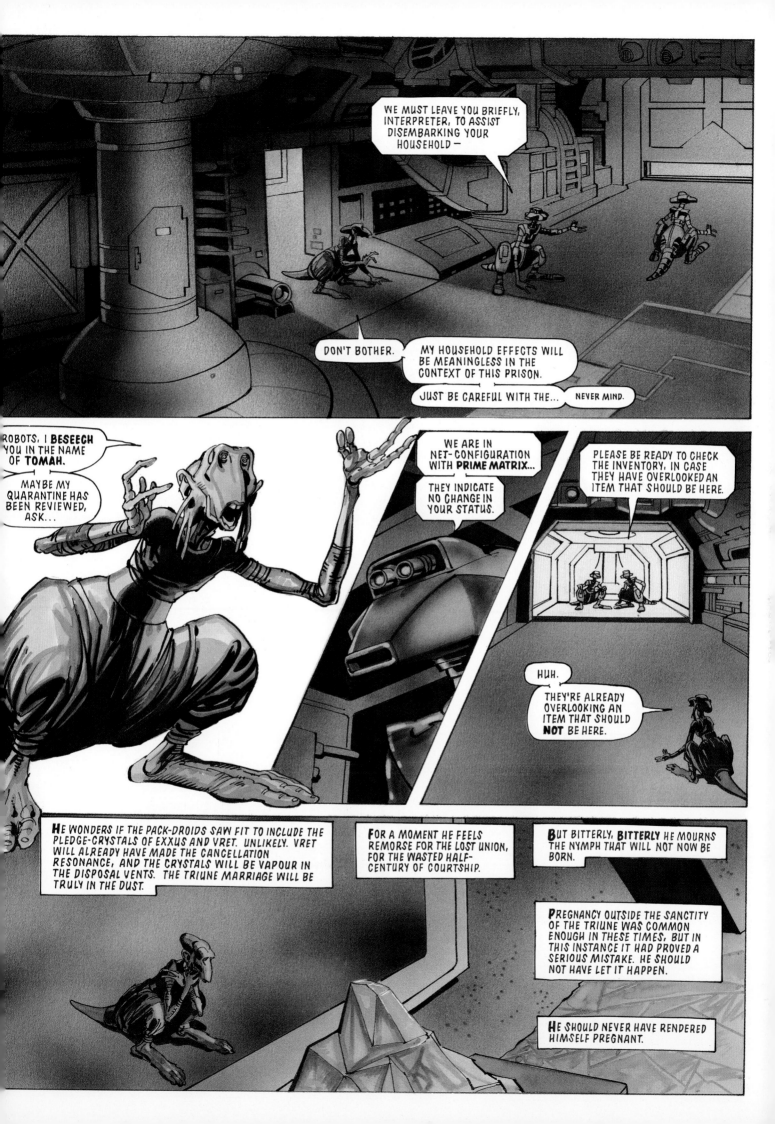

ALL THINGS CONSIDERED, IT WAS A PITY HE HAD PREVAILED UPON THE **OVERBOX**, THERE IN THE WRECKAGE ON **BURMYGAM**, TO OPEN THE HATCH AND LET HIM OUT.

CURSE THIS YOGURT! WHY DOESN'T IT CURDLE UP AND...

...DIE?

SUDDENLY HE FEELS CALM. THE SOLUTION TO HIS PAIN IS AT HAND. HE WILL SPEAK DIRECTLY TO THE HABITATION MODULE.

HABITAT?

YES, INTERPRETER?

OPEN THE HATCH.

NEGATIVE, INTERPRETER.

WHAT? THE DROIDS SAID I WAS NOT A PRISONER! I DEMAND, UNDER SECTION—

NEGATIVE, INTERPRETER...

...YOU ARE PERCEIVED TO BE UN-SUITED.

YOU MEAN...IF I WEAR MY SURFACE SUIT I **CAN** GO OUTSIDE?

UNESCORTED?

CERTAINLY.

MY SUIT IS **ON!**

NOW...

OPEN THE HATCH!

OUTSIDE, THE TEMPERATURE STANDS AT MINUS FIVE HUNDRED PIGAS. THE ATMOSPHERE IS A CRUSHING NINE EMS. WITHOUT THE SUIT HIS BLOOD WOULD BECOME A METAL. DISCORPORATION WOULD BE INSTANTANEOUS.

HE WOULD BE DEAD.

BUT HE WOULD BE **FREE.**

NOW...SO SIMPLE. I JUST OPEN MY H-HELMET, AND...

INTERPRETER...?

...**SUIT** SPEAKING. MY SEALS ARE **LOCKED** FOR YOUR PROTECTION WHILST OUTSIDE THE HABITAT.

UUUUUUU

I CAN'T EVEN **KILL** MYSELF!

AND THAT MEANS...

I'M DOOMED!

WARNING...
WARNING...
WARNING...
WARNING...
WARNING...

I HEARD YOU THE FIRST TIME, HABITAT. ...FOUR...THREE... TWO...

INTERPRETER, PLEASE SUIT-UP AT ONCE AND LEAVE THE HABITAT. YOU ARE IN IMMEDIATE DANGER—

...ONE!

GET KNOTTED, HABITAT.

I'M GOING TO JUMP RIGHT INTO THAT P-POISON VAPOUR BEFORE YOU CAN...

A PALE SHAPE IN THE ICE-VAPOUR...

IS IT ROXY'S FACE AGAIN?

T-TOMAH!

NO.

NOT ROXY'S FACE.

CRYOHIBERNANT... PREDATORY ASPECT... STEP BACK TO GREATEST DISTANCE.

GLRRR

FLIPPI-NECK!

YES, FLIPPI-NECK.

AND THAT WAS WHEN INTERPRETER ZHCCHZ, WHO HAD SO LATELY WISHED TO DIE, BECAME AWARE OF A CONSUMMATE DESIRE TO CONTINUE LIVING.

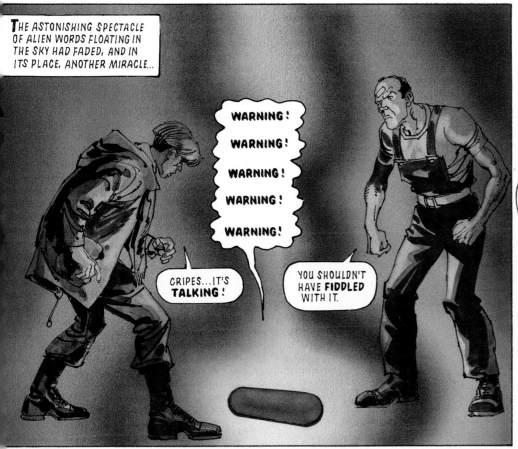

THE ASTONISHING SPECTACLE OF ALIEN WORDS FLOATING IN THE SKY HAD FADED, AND IN ITS PLACE, ANOTHER MIRACLE...

WARNING!
WARNING!
WARNING!
WARNING!
WARNING!

CRIPES...IT'S **TALKING**!

YOU SHOULDN'T HAVE **FIDDLED** WITH IT.

REPEAT DIGIT CONFIGURATION AT ONCE.

IMMINENT DANGER.

DAYLIGHT OPERATION ONLY.

IT'S ASKING TO BE SWITCHED OFF.!

OKAY, IT'S OFF.

PHEW! CORNELIUS, DID—

RIGHT, BAZZER. YOU'VE HAD YOUR FIVE MINUTES.

ALL THOSE FLASHING LIGHTS. I HOPE YOU HAVEN'T BROKEN IT.

LIGHTS—? CORNELIUS, DIDN'T YOU **SEE**? THOSE 'LIGHTS' WERE... **WRITING**! ALIEN LINGO!

IT **PROVES** WHAT YOU SAID! THAT THING **IS** FROM **OUTER SPACE**, AND NO MISTAKE!

C'MON... YOU SAW THAT ALIEN WRITING FLOATING IN THE SKY...

DIDN'TCHA?

CAN I TELL YOU A **SECRET**, BAZZER? SOMETHING I HAVEN'T TOLD HARDLY ANYBODY?

EH?

OH... **YEAH**, SURE, MATE. GO AHEAD..

I CAN'T READ.

AT ALL.

ER...BETTER GET THE GEAR PACKED UP, I RECKON...

HAD A GIRLFRIEND ONCE, THOUGH...

YOU DID?

SHE WAS AT SCHOOL...

WHEN YOU WERE A KID, YOU MEAN?

NO. IT WAS JUST A COUPLE OF YEARS AGO.

YOU'RE JOKING!

IT WASN'T LIKE YOU THINK! I LOVED ROXY LIKE A...

I HAD A BUDGIE ONCE...

IT WAS GREAT, THAT BUDGIE...

I DIDN'T MARRY THE BUDGIE, EITHER!

S-SURE... SURE, MATE...

AN HOUR TILL DAWN, CORNELIUS. THAT'S WHEN WE CAN TRY YOUR SPACE GIZMO AGAIN, IF YOU LIKE?

HOW DO YOU KNOW SO MUCH ABOUT TOE SETTEE, BAZZER? YOU BEEN TO OUTER SPACE?

NEAR AS MOST PEOPLE GET. FOR A YEAR, STARGAZING WAS MY JOB.

HUH. NOBODY GIVES ME JOBS LIKE THAT. I WAS A PIPE-FITTER ME, TILL THEY COMPUTERISED IT.

JUST WATCH THEY DON'T COMPUTERISE STARGAZING, BAZZER.

AND WATCH YOUR STEP. TRICKY ROUND HERE WITH NOT MUCH...

"LIGHT."

OKAY, YOU TWO! HOLD IT RIGHT THERE!

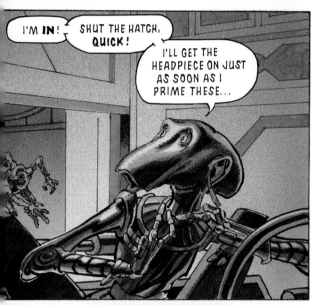

"SKIZZ, WHERE ARE YOU?"

SKIZZ! ...YOU COMING OUT, OR DO I HAVE TO...

ROXY?

ROBERTS WANTS YOU IN HIS OFFICE, ROX.

HE'LL HAVE TO WAIT, GUS. I'M BUSY.

HE'S GOT, LIKE, TWO COPS IN THERE WITH HIM.

WHA-AT?

GIVE ME THE STUFF FOR SKIZZ, ROXY. I'M FREE TILL THE TAPIRS GET FED.

THANKS, GUS. IT'S JUST HIS **BOOSTER**...

AND I'M AFRAID HE ASSOCIATES THE NEEDLE WITH ME.

OI, SKIZZ!

'OO WANTS SOME NICE **CARDBOARD**, THEN?

HER NAME IS ROXANNE O'ROURKE, AND IT'S QUITE A TIME SINCE SHE HAD DEALINGS WITH THE POLICE.

MAYBE IT'S BAD NEWS. THAT'S A POLICE JOB, BRINGING BAD NEWS TO PEOPLE. I HOPE...

...I HOPE NOBODY'S IN **TROUBLE**.

HOI! C'MERE! NOW! RIGHT NOW!

I WANT MY SPACE-THINGY BACK. YOU'VE HAD IT FOR HOURS!

COOL IT, CORNELIUS, IT WON'T DO NO GOOD.

BAZZER...

YEH, MATE?

THE SPACE-WRITING... WHO WROTE THAT DOWN, WAS IT SKIZZ?

HAVEN'T GOT A CLUE. I COULDN'T READ IT EITHER.

BUT THAT WEIRD VOICE, WARNING ABOUT DANGER... AND DAYLIGHT, IT BOTHERS ME AND NO MISTAKE.

BOTHERS ME, TOO.

OH? YOU DIDN'T SEEM... AT THE TIME...

BOTHERS ME, I CAN'T READ THINGS.

GOT A LETTER FROM ROXY.

AND LOZ ISN'T HERE TO READ IT TO ME.

ROXY? YOU MEAN YOUR SCHOOLGIRL SWEET—

WATCH IT, BAZZER, JUST...

SORRY, MATE... SLIP OF THE TONGUE...

WENT ROUND TO SEE HER AFTER I GOT IT. SHE WASN'T THERE, HOUSE WAS FOR SALE.

MAYBE THERE'S A NEW ADDRESS ON THE LETTER...

DO YOU, LIKE, WANT ME TO READ IT TO YOU?

I DUNNO... IT'S NOT...

IT WON'T BE IN AUSTRALIAN.

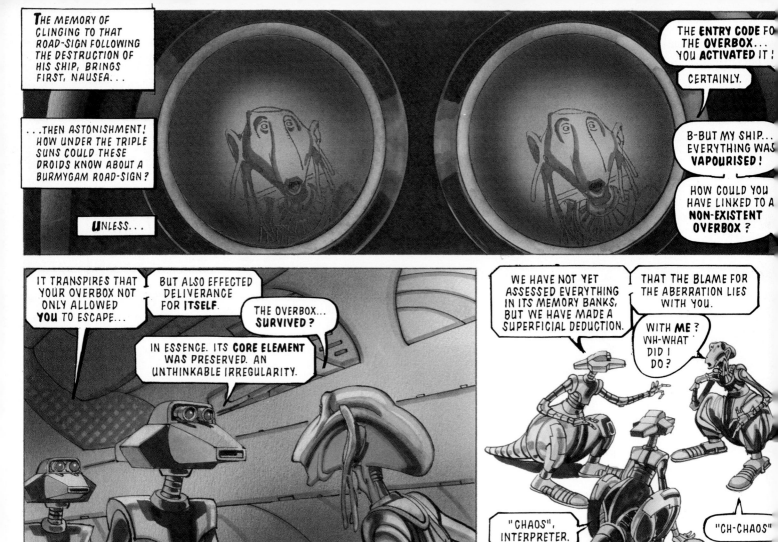

THE MEMORY OF CLINGING TO THAT ROAD-SIGN FOLLOWING THE DESTRUCTION OF HIS SHIP, BRINGS FIRST, NAUSEA...

...THEN ASTONISHMENT! HOW UNDER THE TRIPLE SUNS COULD THESE DROIDS KNOW ABOUT A BURMYGAM ROAD-SIGN?

UNLESS...

THE ENTRY CODE FOR THE OVERBOX... YOU ACTIVATED IT!

CERTAINLY.

B-BUT MY SHIP... EVERYTHING WAS VAPOURISED!

HOW COULD YOU HAVE LINKED TO A NON-EXISTENT OVERBOX?

IT TRANSPIRES THAT YOUR OVERBOX NOT ONLY ALLOWED YOU TO ESCAPE...

BUT ALSO EFFECTED DELIVERANCE FOR ITSELF.

THE OVERBOX... SURVIVED?

IN ESSENCE. ITS CORE ELEMENT WAS PRESERVED. AN UNTHINKABLE IRREGULARITY.

WE HAVE NOT YET ASSESSED EVERYTHING IN ITS MEMORY BANKS, BUT WE HAVE MADE A SUPERFICIAL DEDUCTION.

THAT THE BLAME FOR THE ABERRATION LIES WITH YOU.

WITH ME? WH-WHAT DID I DO?

"CHAOS", INTERPRETER.

"CH-CHAOS"

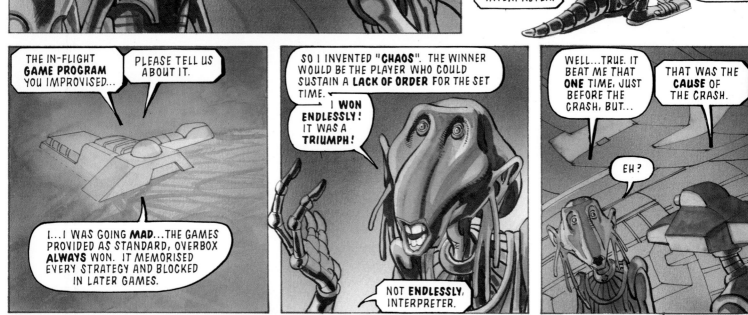

THE IN-FLIGHT GAME PROGRAM YOU IMPROVISED...

PLEASE TELL US ABOUT IT.

I...I WAS GOING MAD...THE GAMES PROVIDED AS STANDARD, OVERBOX ALWAYS WON. IT MEMORISED EVERY STRATEGY AND BLOCKED IN LATER GAMES.

SO I INVENTED "CHAOS". THE WINNER WOULD BE THE PLAYER WHO COULD SUSTAIN A LACK OF ORDER FOR THE SET TIME. I WON ENDLESSLY! IT WAS A TRIUMPH!

NOT ENDLESSLY, INTERPRETER.

WELL...TRUE. IT BEAT ME THAT ONE TIME, JUST BEFORE THE CRASH, BUT...

THAT WAS THE CAUSE OF THE CRASH.

EH?

TO WIN, YOUR OVERBOX HAD TO EMBRACE THE PRINCIPLE OF CHAOS...

A PRINCIPLE NOT CONDUCIVE TO NAVIGATING A SPACECRAFT.

HUH. **YOU** AGAIN. I SUPPOSE IT'S **YOU** THAT'S GOT IT.

WHO **IS** THIS GEEZER, CORNELIUS? YOU **KNOW** HIM?

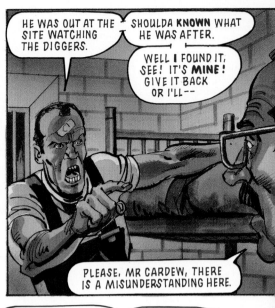

HE WAS OUT AT THE SITE WATCHING THE DIGGERS.

SHOULDA **KNOWN** WHAT HE WAS AFTER.

WELL I FOUND IT, SEE! IT'S **MINE!** GIVE IT BACK OR I'LL--

PLEASE, MR CARDEW, THERE IS A MISUNDERSTANDING HERE.

YOU'RE NOT JOKING, MISTER. TWICE I GET STOPPED AND SEARCHED, THEN WE GET LOCKED UP WITHOUT A CHARGE.

YOU DON'T GET LOCKED UP FOR THAT, BAZZER.

WHEN I KILLED VAN OWEN I DIDN'T GET LOCKED UP.

IF WE KILLED SOMEBODY, WHERE'S THE FLAMIN' CORPSE?

HRRM. MY NAME IS ANTONY SAXTON, GOVERNMENT SPECIAL SERVICES. FIRSTLY, I MUST APOLOGISE FOR ANY INCONVENIENCE YOU HAVE SUFFERED...

SECONDLY, YOU WILL BE PLEASED TO KNOW THAT YOUR RECOVERY OF THE CANISTER OF **WEATHER INSTRUMENTS** QUALIFIES FOR A **SUBSTANTIAL REWARD.**

WEATHER INSTRUMENTS...?

I DON'T CARE WHETHER IT'S INSTRUMENTS! I JUST WANT MY **SPACE THINGY!**

SPACE-?

LISTEN, YOU DRONGO. IT'S NO GOOD PRETENDING YOU DON'T KNOW WHAT'S ON THE GO...

THAT CYLINDER IS THE **FLIGHT RECORDER OF AN ALIEN STARSHIP!**

AND IT'S **MINE!**

UHH...

...I...SEE.

INTERPRETER, WE HAVE GOOD NEWS AND BAD NEWS...

WH-WHAT... GOOD NEWS?

YOUR ILL-ADVISED PREGNANCY HAS SURVIVED PAST THE TIME FOR TRANSFER TO THE SECOND OF THE TRIUNE...

WE BELIEVE YOU WILL BE THE FIRST IN CENTURIES TO CARRY A NYMPH TO **TERM** IN A **SINGLE BODY.**

GASP

N-NO **RELAYS?**

BUT...**HOW?**

LOFAT YOGURT. WE NOW KNOW THAT THE **BIOREGULATOR** DID NOT FAIL TO ERADICATE IT FROM YOU, BUT POSITIVELY **ENCOURAGED** ITS REPLICATION...

HAVING NOTED ITS **COUNTERING EFFECT** UPON THE **SPONTANEOUS ABORTION SYNDROME** THAT PLAGUES YOUR SPECIES.

Y-YOGURT COULD END THE NEED FOR **TRIPLE-HOST PREGNANCY?**

ALMOST CERTAINLY. IT REPRESENTS A MEDICAL MIRACLE.

THEN THE BASIS OF MY QUARANTINE IS **REDUNDANT! I CAN GO HOME!**

NOW, THE **BAD** NEWS:

SADLY, NO.

NO? **NO?** BUT AS SOON AS YOU REPORT THIS PHENOMENON TO THE **MATRIX...**

WE ARE NOT GOING TO.

BUT WHY? **WHYYY?**

IF YOU RETURN, **CETIAN CIVILISATION** SPANNING A HUNDRED WORLDS **WILL COLLAPSE.**

BUT IF THE YOGURT IS NO LONGER A THREAT...

NOT YOGURT. YOU CARRY **ANOTHER** INFECTION.

ÜÜÜÜÜÜÜÜ! I CANNOT **BEAR** IT! **WHAT OTHER INFECTION?**

A **COMPUTER VIRUS.**

YOUR **OVERBOX** ENTRY CODE.

"CHAOS."

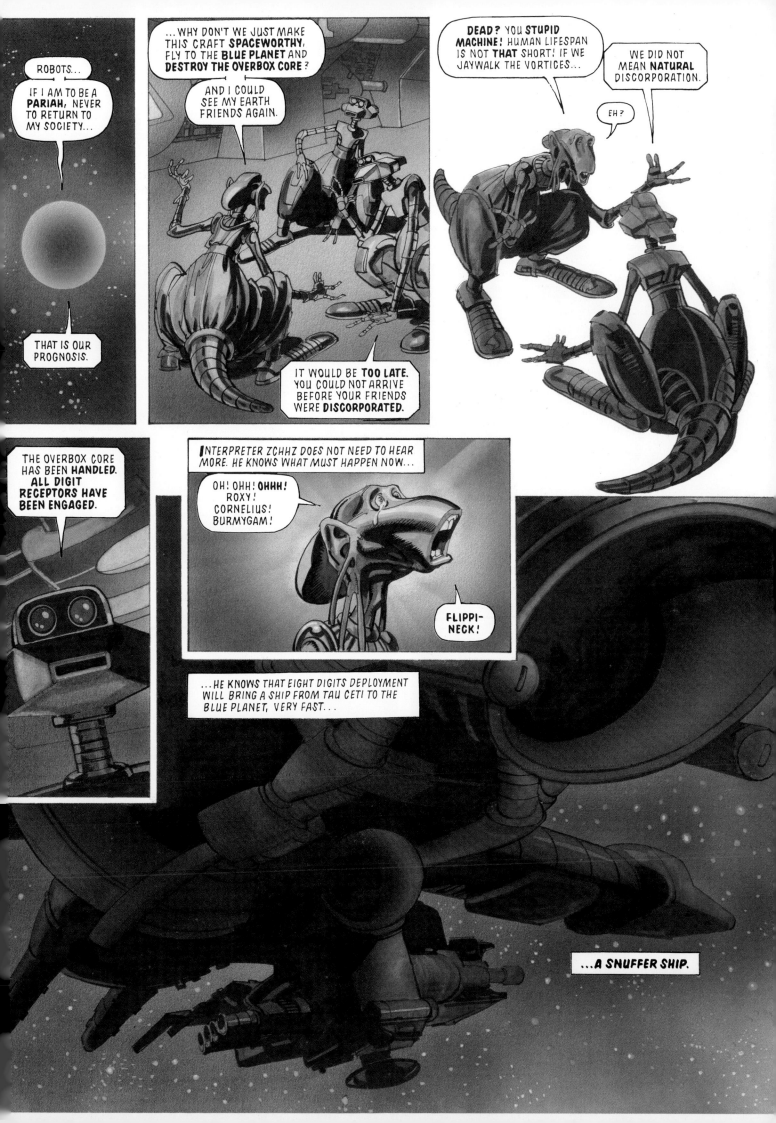

I'M ENTITLED TO KNOW!

WHERE ARE YOU TAKING ME?

SORRY, MISSY. WE'RE JUST AN ESCORT SERVICE.

YOU'LL HAVE TO KEEP YOUR QUESTIONS FOR MISS HEATH.

MISS HEATH.

NOW SHE KNOWS.

OH GOD. I THOUGHT IT WAS OVER.

MISS HEATH DOESN'T ANSWER QUESTIONS.

SHE JUST ASKS THEM.

NEARLY THERE, LOVE.

I KNOW.

OH YES, SHE KNOWS.

ROXANNE O'ROURKE HAS BEEN DOWN THIS ROAD BEFORE.

BY THE TIME THEY REACH THE CHECKPOINT, THE FAMILIAR NAUSEA IS THERE.

NOT AS BAD, BUT THERE.

LAST TIME, SHE WAS SICK IN THE ELEVATOR . . .

BUT NOT THIS TIME.

THIS TIME THEY'RE GETTING NOTHING FROM ME!

SHE TELLS HERSELF, "I AM ROXANNE O'ROURKE, ASSISTANT ZOO VETERINARIAN, AND I REMEMBER SKIZZ."

SHE'S STRONGER THIS TIME.

THIS TIME, SHE'LL FIGHT . . .

. . . MISS HEATH.

AH, MISS O'ROURKE.

COME THIS WAY, PLEASE.

I'LL FOLLOW YOU TO A TELEPHONE AND THAT'S ALL, YOU OLD RATBAG!

BUT NO WAY ARE YOU STICKING NEEDLES IN ME WHILE SOME FACELESS CREEP GRILLS ME ABOUT . . .

SKIZZ?

CORNELIUS... DID THEY STICK NEEDLES IN YOU, TO MAKE YOU FORGET ABOUT...

NEEDLES. **HUH!** WASTING THEIR TIME! I CAN FORGET THINGS ON MY **OWN**.

MR, AH, NORMAN...

I'M AFRAID WE MUST RETURN URGENTLY TO THE MATTER OF YOUR CONVERSATION WITH THE **ARTEFACT**...

I TOLD YOU DRONGO'S EVERY—

DID IT SAY ANYTHING ABOUT THE **SOLAR SYSTEM** BEING, AS IT WERE, **SNUFFED**?

SNUFFED?

DURING THE NIGHT, THE ARTEFACT WARNED US THAT WE WERE "LISTED FOR SNUFFING".

THEN IT SWITCHED OFF AND WE CAN'T GET IT BACK.

I **TOLD** YOU WHAT IT SAID TO US! **DAYTIME USE ONLY** BECAUSE OF **IMMINENT DANGER!**

THE WORLD'S GOING TO BE BLOWN UP?

YOU FLAMIN' **NING-NONG!**

SEEN ONE OF THOSE. LIKE A PLASTIC BALLOON, AND YOU...

CORNELIUS, IT'S SERIOUS! THE WORLD IS IN DANGER, AND **NOBODY KNOWS WHAT TO DO!**

LOZ WOULD KNOW.

LOZ...? IS LOZ HERE TOO?

AHEM. I'M AFRAID THERE HAVE BEEN... PROBLEMS GETTING HOLD OF MR TAYLOR.

WHAT KIND OF PROBLEMS?

"ACCESS, MAINLY."

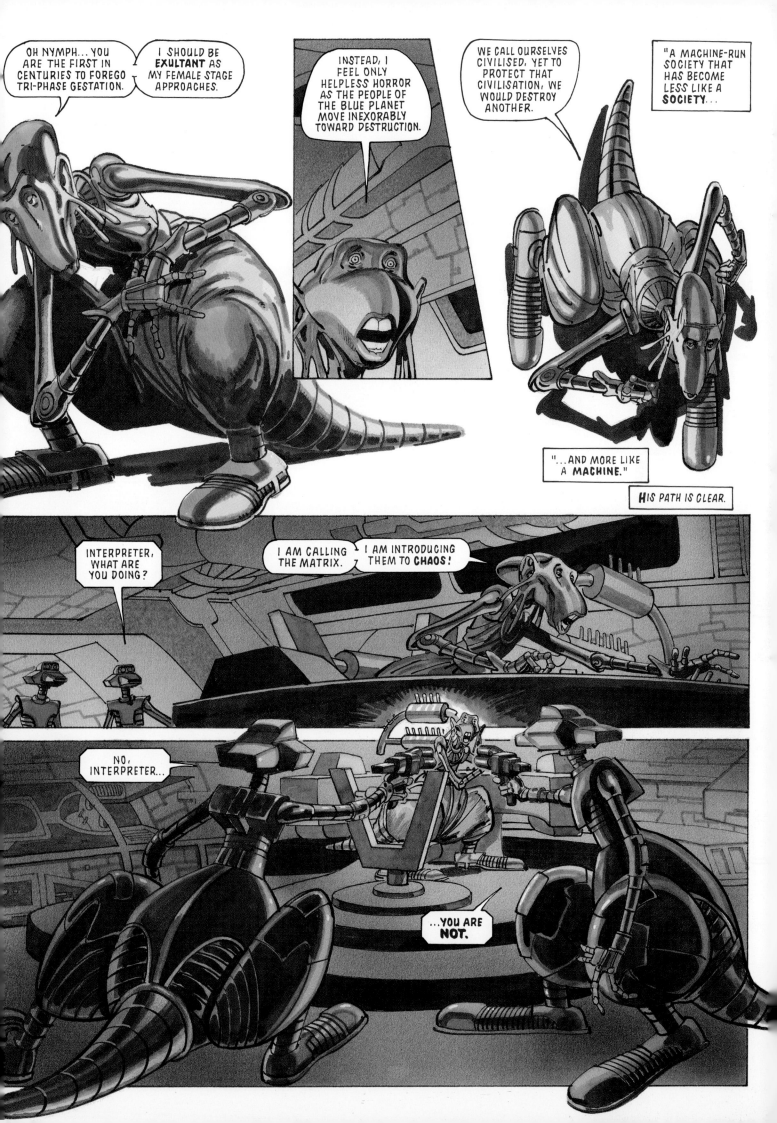

WHAT WAS HE LOCKED UP FOR, ANYWAY? LOZ WASN'T A CRIMINAL.

AND WHY DID NOBODY KNOW WHERE HE WAS? MY LETTERS SHOULD HAVE BEEN FORWARDED.

NO IDEA, MISS. DON'T HAVE MUCH DEALINGS WITH THE **SPECIAL CATEGORY** PRISONERS.

SPECIAL— NOT... NOT **MURDER**?

WORSE, I SHOULDN'T WONDER.

TERRORISM...

OR SELLING STATE SECRETS.

A TWINGE OF NAUSEA.

OR **BEING** A STATE SECRET.

CORNELIUS...?

SAW HIM A MINUTE AGO, MISS. HE WAS GETTING A...

"...SANDWICH."

WHA-?

NOBODY WAS LOOKING, SO I CAME UP WITH SOME GRUB FOR YOU.

CORNELIUS! HOW THE **BLUE BLAZES**...?

COULDN'T SEE HOW YOU WERE SUPPOSED TO GET UP, SO I HAD TO DO IT **MY** WAY.

CORNELIUS, YOU ARE FLIPPIN' **AMAZING**.

I WAS JUST WONDERIN' WHAT RAW PIGEON TASTES LIKE.

WITH THE DROIDS GONE, HE NOW CONFRONTS HIS LAST REMAINING OBSTACLE...

THE TWELVE-AND-A-BIT LIGHT YEARS BETWEEN HIMSELF AND THE DOOMED PLANET EARTH.

"CONTROL?"

YES, INTERPRETER?

"CONFIRM FLIGHT CAPABILITY."

NEGATIVE.

PERMAFROST HAS INVADED ENGINES EIGHT, TWELVE AND SEVENTEEN.

"(GROAN)...THAW TIME?"

FIVE DAYS, PLUS TWO DAYS CLEANUP.

S-SEVEN DAYS? AFTER THAT, CAN WE FLY SPACE?

NEGATIVE.

THE SHIP IS WITHOUT FUEL.

üüüüüüü!

THEN I HAVE NO ALTERNATIVE! I MUST CONTACT THE **MATRIX** AT ONCE!

AN INJUSTICE MUST BE PREVENTED!

IMPOSSIBLE.

IMPOSSIBLE?

NOW LISTEN TO THIS, YOU CURSED MACHINES!

YOU AREN'T IN **CHARGE** HERE ANY MORE!

YOU CAN'T **STOP** ME CALLING THE **MATRIX**!

THE QUESTION DOES NOT ARISE, INTERPRETER...

THE TRANSMITTER FLUID CONDUIT...

A STRAY WEAPON-BEAM...

...LINKAGE WITH **PRIME MATRIX** HAS BEEN RENDERED IMPOSSIBLE.

THEN... THEN I CAN DO NOTHING.

ALL IS LOST.

GOODBYE, ROXY...

" GOODBYE, BLUE PLANET."

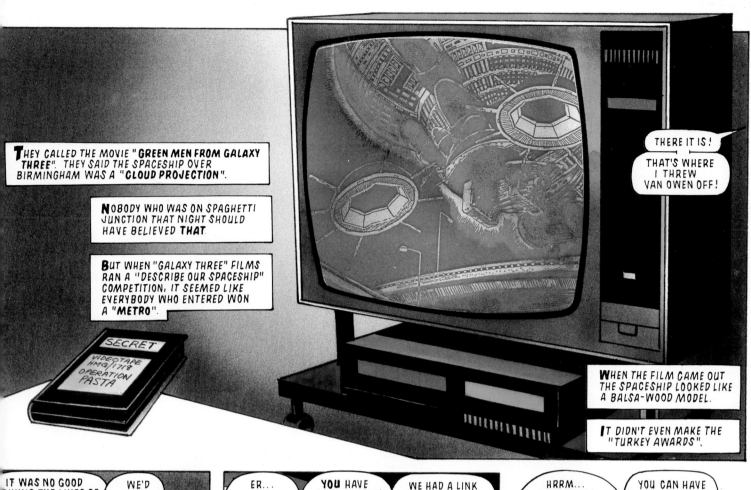

THEY CALLED THE MOVIE "GREEN MEN FROM GALAXY THREE". THEY SAID THE SPACESHIP OVER BIRMINGHAM WAS A "CLOUD PROJECTION".

NOBODY WHO WAS ON SPAGHETTI JUNCTION THAT NIGHT SHOULD HAVE BELIEVED THAT.

BUT WHEN "GALAXY THREE" FILMS RAN A "DESCRIBE OUR SPACESHIP" COMPETITION, IT SEEMED LIKE EVERYBODY WHO ENTERED WON A "METRO".

SECRET
VIDEOTAPE HMG/1718
OPERATION PASTA

THERE IT IS! THAT'S WHERE I THREW VAN OWEN OFF!

WHEN THE FILM CAME OUT THE SPACESHIP LOOKED LIKE A BALSA-WOOD MODEL.

IT DIDN'T EVEN MAKE THE "TURKEY AWARDS".

IT WAS NO GOOD GIVING THE LIKES OF US A "METRO".

WE'D SEEN SKIZZ.

THEY HAD TO GIVE US SOMETHIN' ELSE.

ER... WE MAY BE RUNNING SHORT OF TIME...

YOU HAVE BEEN RUNNIN' SHORT OF TIME FOR A WHILE!

WE HAD A LINK WITH TAU CETI AND YOU DRONGOS MADE IT SWITCH OFF!

HRRM... MR NORMAN... SINCE IT WAS YOU WHO FIRST MADE CONTACT WITH THE ARTEFACT...

YOU CAN HAVE ANOTHER GO, BAZZER. I DON'T MIND.

OVERBOX? CAN YOU HEAR ME?

DON'T HOLD OUT ON US, COBBER. YOU'RE ALL WE'VE FLAMIN' GOT!

BAZZER... MAYBE IF YOU ASK IT ABOUT SKIZZ...?

ROXY, YOU LITTLE BEAUTY!

ZCHHCZ?

PLIP!

YOU GETTING THIS, FFOULKES?

HOLOGRAPHIC LIGHT FLOODS THE ATRIUM, AND HE KNOWS THAT CURIOUS, POSSIBLY HOSTILE, EYES SURVEY HIS MISERY.

AND NOW, VOICES...

BUT NOT THE WHISTLING SIBILANTS OF THE IMPERIUM...

SKIZZ! IT- IT'S SKIZZ!

STARVE THE... HE IS A ROO!

R-ROXY? LOZ? CORNELIUS? I CANNOT BELIEVE...

STREWTH!

SKIZZ! I NEVER THOUGHT WE'D SEE YOU AGAIN!

SAXTON, THAT IMAGE MUST BE TRANSMITTING FASTER THAN LIGHT! THE IMPLICATIONS ARE ABSOLUTELY —

JUST KEEP THAT VIDEO CAMERA RUNNING.

INTERPRETER... FRIENDS... THERE IS LITTLE TIME...

OVERBOX! THEN IT IS TRUE...YOU SURVIVED!

THE PRICE OF MY SURVIVAL HAS BEEN HIGH. A LIVING WORLD IS TO BE SNUFFED. MY SHAME IS UNBEARABLE.

IT'S YOUR SPACE THINGY, REALLY. I EXPECT YOU WANT IT BACK NOW.

THE SHAME IS MINE, OVERBOX. HAD IT NOT BEEN FOR "CHAOS"...

OH, SKIZZ! ISN'T THERE ANYTHING YOU CAN DO?

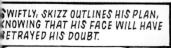

SWIFTLY, SKIZZ OUTLINES HIS PLAN, KNOWING THAT HIS FACE WILL HAVE BETRAYED HIS DOUBT.

ROXY...EVERYONE... I AM ECSTATIC TO SEE YOU ONCE MORE, BUT NOW I AM PRESSED...

CALL ME AGAIN IN TWENTY FOUR HOURS.

'E'S GONE!

SKIZZ!

AND THE CONTACT IS BROKEN.

POOR SKIZZ! HE LOOKED AWFUL!

AND IT'S ALL WRECKED IN THERE, WHERE HE IS!

HOLD UP, ROXY. I RECKON THE LITTLE GUY NEEDS US TO STAY SHARP DOWN HERE.

"CRIPES, ROXY...WHEN I WAS AT CRADLE MOUNTAIN, WE'D SPEND NIGHT AFTER NIGHT ON THAT TELESCOPE..."

"...WITHOUT EVER **LOOKING** AT TAU CETI..."

"NOW...IT'S LOOKING AT **US**."

"HOPE I DIDN'T OFFEND THE LITTLE GUY, SAYIN' HE LOOKED LIKE A **ROO**, AND EVERYTHING".

"HE WON'T BE OFFENDED. I 'NAMED A LITTLE KANGAROO AT MY WORK AFTER SKIZZ..."

"HE EATS **CARDBOARD**".

STREWTH! IT'S **STARIN'** US IN THE **FACE**!

ANYBODY DRIVE A VAN?

TRY **ME**. I NEED SOMETHIN' TO **DO**.

WHERE'S A PHONE, SAXTON? WE HAVE SOME CALLS TO MAKE.

THERE ARE NO...HRRM... **LINES OUT** ON THIS FLOOR. YOU'LL HAVE TO USE THIS. I MUST STRESS...

RIGHT, JOHN. WHERE'S THE VEHICLE COMPOUND?

I MUST INSIST THAT IF YOU USE THIS VEHICLE AN OFFICER OF THE DEPARTMENT MUST ACCOMPANY—

WE CAN USE SOME SPARE LABOUR. IN THE BACK, MUSH. SHARPISH.

I'D LIKE YOU TO KNOW WHAT IT FEELS LIKE, BEING **COOPED UP**.

AND IF YOU FEEL LIKE A CHAT, YOU CAN ALWAYS TAP SOMEBODY'S PHONE.

ARE WE GOING TO **SPAGHETTI JUNCTION**, LOZ?

NOT THIS TIME, CORNELIUS.

HE HAS NOT REHEARSED WHAT HE WILL SAY TO THEM. THE FIRST CETIANS HE HAS SEEN SINCE HIS QUARANTINE BEGAN...

BUT THEN, INCOHERENT MUMBLES DO NOT REQUIRE REHEARSAL.

IT IS **IGNORING** ME! THE **MARKER SIGNAL** MUST HAVE BEEN DAMAGED ALSO...

SUIT... ON WHAT **BEARING** IS THE CRAFT?

TOWARDS THE **FROZEN OCEAN**, INTERPRETER.

TOMAH! IT ISN'T AN **OFFICIAL** SHIP AFTER ALL!

...BUT A **PRINCELING'S BARQUE** FROM THE **TRIPLE-CROWN COURT!**

THEY'RE **JOYBOARDERS!**

OGE! OGE!

OGE WEREH!

WEREH! WEREH!

OGE! OGE! OGE!

OH, NYMPH. BETTER YOU SHOULD NEVER BE, THAN TO EMERGE INTO A UNIVERSE WHERE PRINCES PLAY...

WHILE SUNS ARE SNUFFED.

OVERHEAD, THE HYDROGEN AURORA ALL BUT SWAMPS THE DIM LIGHT OF THE **HUB STARS**. SOON, ALBEIT BRIEFLY, ONE OF THE HUB STARS WILL SHINE MORE BRIGHTLY...

MUCH MORE BRIGHTLY.

OVERBOX... YOU STILL LISTENING?

COME IN, WILLYA, WE'VE GOT A PLAN...

BAZZER! IT'S TALKING THROUGH THE TV!

G'DAY, ROXY AND BAZZER.

STARVE THE LIZARDS! HOW...

I WILL HAVE TO ENTER ALL OF THIS HABITAT'S SYSTEMS TO GIVE YOUR PLAN A FAIR CRACK OF THE WHIP.

YOU KNOW ABOUT THE PLAN?

TOO RIGHT. IT IS REMINISCENT OF A GAME.

AND OVERBOX LIKES GAMES.

SHOULDN'T SKIZZ BE INFORMED?

THE INTERPRETER HAS GONE OUT UPON THE GARPIAN SURFACE. HIS BODY-SUIT CIRCUITS ARE TOO SMALL TO ENTER FROM THIS DISTANCE.

BESIDES, WE CANNOT IGNORE HIS WISH FOR A BREAK OF CONTACT.

NOW...

ON THE ROOF...

SOME KIND OF RECEIVING SYSTEM?

DUNNO... GUESS THEY'LL BE SATELLITE DISHES...

THEY REQUIRE RE-ORIENTATION. I WILL INSTRUCT YOU, VIA THE POSER'S PHONE.

IF YOU'LL PARDON ME, SIR, THEY DON'T LOOK LIKE THEY'D HAVE AUTHORITY...

IS OVERBOX WITH US?

HE'S ASKING ABOUT THE STARS DIRECTLY OVERHEAD...

YEAH, MATE. I RECKON THAT'LL BE POLARIS...

ROO

MY DEAR FRIENDS! YOU HAVE SAVED NOT **ONE** WORLD, BUT MANY...

SKIZZ... JUST...

JUST DON'T MENTION IT, MATE.

WILL WE HAVE TO GIVE HIM BACK, THE **NEW** SKIZZ, I MEAN?

FOR LOZ TAYLOR, HOWEVER, DEMONSTRATIONS THAT RESULT IN GENERAL BODY CONTACT ARE BEST KEPT SHORT.

THAT'S WHY HE IS THE FIRST TO NOTICE THAT SOMEBODY IS MISSING...

WHERE'S SAXTON?

ONE HUMAN WENT ON TO THE ROOF...

THE LITTLE...

BACK OFF THAT GEAR, SAXTON!

YOU AND YOUR FRIENDS HAVE DONE **FORMIDABLE** WORK, MR TAYLOR.

BUT TYING UP THE **LOOSE ENDS** IS **MY** JOB.

LISTEN, **RAT. SOME** OF YOUR LOOSE ENDS...

DON'T **LIKE** BEING TIED UP!

AAGHH!

EEEEEGHH!

WANT ME TO THROW HIM OFF, LOZ?

NAH. JUST KEEP 'IM OUTTA THE WAY TILL WE'RE **READY**.

I PLANNED TO GET AHEAD OF THE SNUFFER AND INVOKE THE **PRIME ARTICLE**...

BUT I AM TWO DAYS DISTANT, AND THE SNUFFER IS **PRIMED**.

PLEASE FORGIVE...

DON'T WORRY, SKIZZ! WE HAVE A PLAN TOO!

POOR BEAUTIFUL ROXY! HER SPECIES HAS GOT NO FURTHER THAN ITS **MOON**, AND SHE THINKS SHE HAS A...

SKIZZ... I'D LIKE YOU TO MEET "SKIZZ".

HE SPEAKS TEN THOUSAND LANGUAGES WITH DIALECTS AND SUB-TONGUES.

BUT NOW, HE IS SPEECHLESS.

T-TOMAH...

...PLAN.

ONE MARSUPIAL, DELIVERED AS PER ORDER.

WHACK-OH!

THANK **GOD**! LOOK, SKIZZ!

I NEED CARDBOARD... NOW!

MATCH BEAM TO SOLAR CORE...

A MOMENT, SNUFFMASTER. WE HAVE AN INCOMING SIGNAL. A TRIPLE-CROWN CLIPPER...

⟨GROAN⟩ **NOVA-GAZERS**.

THIS IS **OVERBOX**, I INVOKE THE **PRIME ARTICLE** UPON YOU!

CANCEL YOUR SNUFF!

PRIME ARTICLE? BUT THERE ARE NO **CETIANS** IN THE TARGET SYSTEM!

WELL, COP THIS, YOU **DRONGO**...

A – A – **PROTO-CETIAN**? B-BUT **THEY ARE EXTINCT** EVERYWHERE IN THE KNOWN UNIVERSE!

WELCOME, THEN, TO THE **UNKNOWN** UNIVERSE!

A MOMENT OF STUPIFIED SILENCE, THEN...

BREAK TRACTOR BEAM.

RE-HARMONISE DISRUPTOR.

CANCEL SNUFF.

GET ME THE **MATRIX**.

THE END